Eleven Plus
Secondary School Selection

Mathematics

11+
Daily Practice Tests

20 Tests
Dual Format

Introduction

This book is designed to complement the IPS set of 11+ mathematics practice papers. It contains short daily practice papers, and uses questions of all of the types covered in the IPS range.

When practising for tests such as the 11+, or other school entrance exams, most people do not use full length practice papers on a daily basis. However, a few minutes of practice every day can be very beneficial, and it does not put too much strain on the pupil who will sit the exam – which is very important indeed.

We would suggest using these papers in between attempting longer practice papers.

Each test should be completed in about six minutes. All the question types used in the IPS range of publications are used in this book. In order to fit the questions on each page we have not left much room for working out. We suggest you use some scrap paper if you need to.

Good luck.

11+ Team 2005

Daily Test 1

Score. _______

Question 1

49	65	81
65	81	97
81	97	

There is a number missing on this grid.

What is it? (_____)

Write your answer in the space provided or mark the appropriate number on your answer sheet.

Question 2

Look at the diagram below:

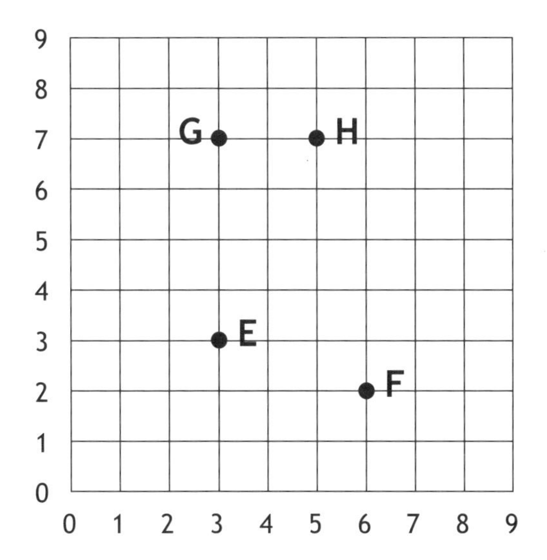

What are the co-ordinates of the points at letter F and letter G?

F ____ , ____

G ____ , ____

Write the co-ordinates in the spaces provided or mark the appropriate pair your answer sheet.

Question 3

Jim's father is 3 times as old as Jim was 5 years ago.

If Jim's father is 45, how old is Jim? ________

Write your answer in the space provided or mark the appropriate number on your answer sheet.

Question 4

Which of these sets of numbers contains all square numbers?

A.	16	36	56	☐
B.	46	49	72	☐
C.	36	64	90	☐
D.	36	49	144	☐
E.	72	120	144	☐

Place a cross in the box or mark the appropriate letter on your answer sheet.

Question 5

Look at the Venn diagram below. It shows how many children in Miss Roger's class play tennis, rounders or both. 4 children play neither. There are 36 children in the class.

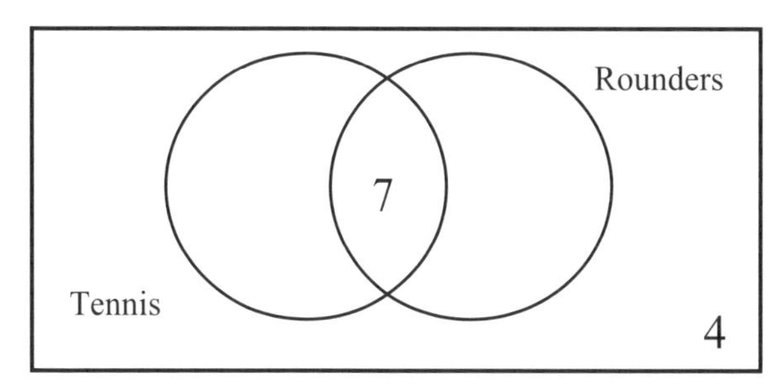

If 18 children play tennis:

How many children in the class play rounders?

(_____)

Write your answer in the space provided or mark the appropriate number on your answer sheet.

Question 6

In this question you must find the missing number so that the equation balances.

$$64 \div 8 \times 3 = 39 \div 3 + \_\_\_\_\_\_$$

Write your answer in the space provided or mark the appropriate number on your answer sheet.

Daily Test 2

Score. _______

Question 1

Jacqueline has three 50 pence pieces, four 20 pence pieces three 10 pence pieces and a 5 pence piece in her pocket.

How much money does she have in total?

£ ___________

Write your answer in the space provided or mark the appropriate number on your answer sheet.

Question 2

This is a map of the tunnels under Vernon Castle. You must try to find your way from the Kitchen to the lounge using a set of instructions.

Key to the instructions:
FD means forward, **RT** means turn right 90º and **LT** means turn left 90º.

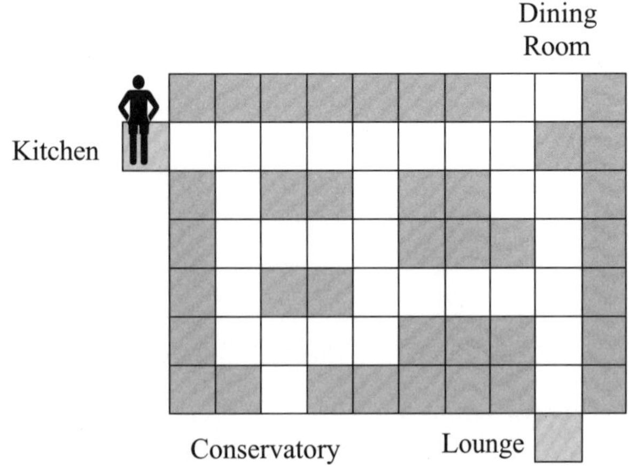

Which of these sets of instructions is the correct one? Circle the appropriate letter or mark the appropriate letter on your answer sheet.

A. FD 5, RT, FD 3, RT, FD 4, RT, FD 3.

B. FD 8 , LT, FD 5, LT, FD 2, RT, FD 6.

C. FD 2, LT, FD 3, RT, FD 5, RT, FD 3.

D. FD 5, RT, FD 3, LT, FD 4, RT, FD 3.

E. FD 2, RT, FD 3, LT, FD 8, RT, FD 6.

Question 3

There are 16 mini chocolate bars in a packet.

How many packets would you fill with 336 bars?

________ packets

Write your answer in the space provided or mark the appropriate number on your answer sheet.

Question 4

Jenny works as a waitress. In the last four days she has made lots of money in tips. She adds up the total four days tips. £2.75, £3.55, £4.65 and £3.95.

How much are the tips worth in total?

£ _________

Place a cross in the box or mark the appropriate letter on your answer sheet.

Question 5

This graph shows the conversion rate between UK Pounds (£) and US Dollars ($).

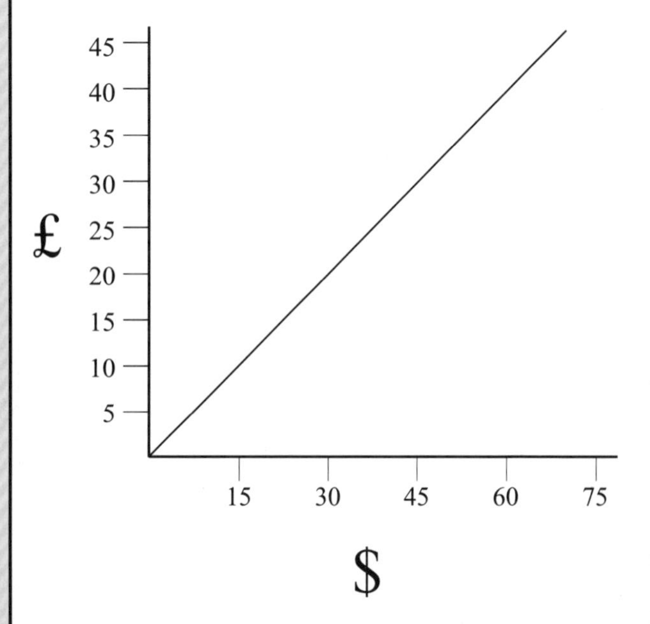

How many dollars ($) would I need to change to get £30?

$ ______

Write your answer in the space provided or mark the appropriate amount on your answer sheet.

Question 6

Ayleston Rovers Juniors played the Wickan Rangers Juniors in a football match.

The match kicked off at 2.15 p.m. They played 35 minutes each half, and had a half-time break of 10 minutes.

At what time did the match end? __________

Write your answer in the space provided or mark the appropriate time on your answer sheet.

Daily Test 3

Score. ______

Question 1

Look at the net below. When folded it makes a box.

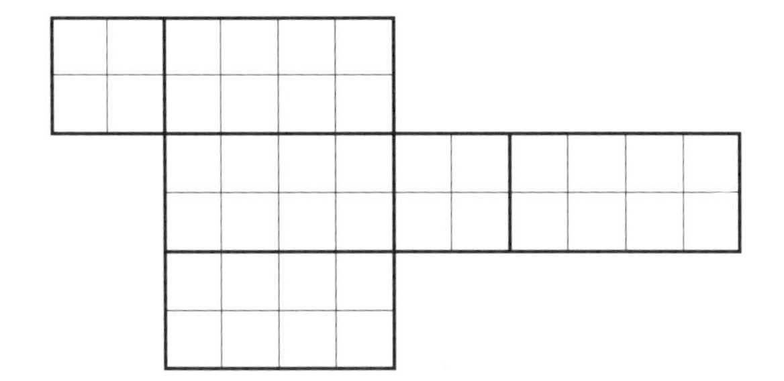

If the side of each small square is 2 cm, what will be the total surface area of the box?

________ cm^2

Write your answer in the space provided or mark the appropriate number on your answer sheet.

Question 2

There are 36 children on a bus - 20 girls and 16 boys. One child's name is chosen at random to collect the tickets.

What is the chance that the child will be a girl?

(Show your answer as a fraction in its lowest terms.)

____

Write your answer in the space provided or mark the appropriate number on your answer sheet.

Question 3

120 children took part in a "Guess the weight of the box of sweets" competition.

⅝ guessed too high. ¼ guessed too low.

How many children guessed the correct weight of the box of sweets?

____

Write your answer in the space provided or mark the appropriate number on your answer sheet.

Question 4

This is Geoff's function machine.

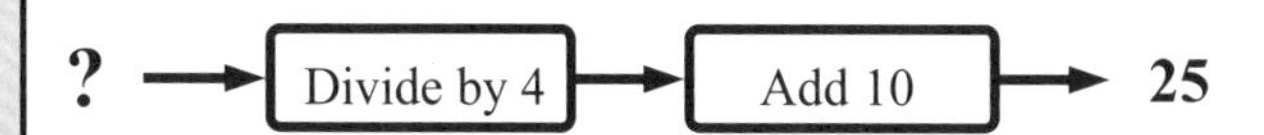

What number did he start with?

____

Write your answer in the space provided or mark the appropriate number on your answer sheet.

Question 5

Mary, Theresa. June and Jessica all stood for election to become Head Girl.

200 children in the school voted for which girl they wanted to be the Head Girl. The percentages of votes cast are shown in the pie chart below.

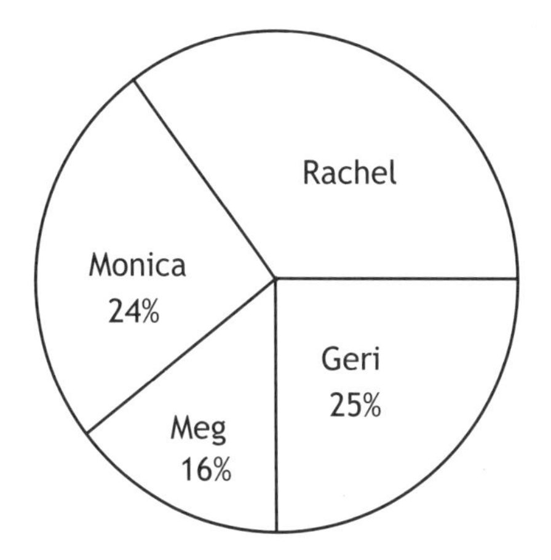

How many votes did Rachel receive? ________

Write your answer in the space provided or mark the appropriate number on your answer sheet.

Question 6

How should 10.30 in the evening be written in the 24 hour clock?

____

Write your answer in the space provided or mark the appropriate time on your answer sheet.

Daily Test 4

Score. _______

Question 1

Five children spend their weekend delivering leaflets advertising the school fete. The bar chart below shows how many each of the children delivered.

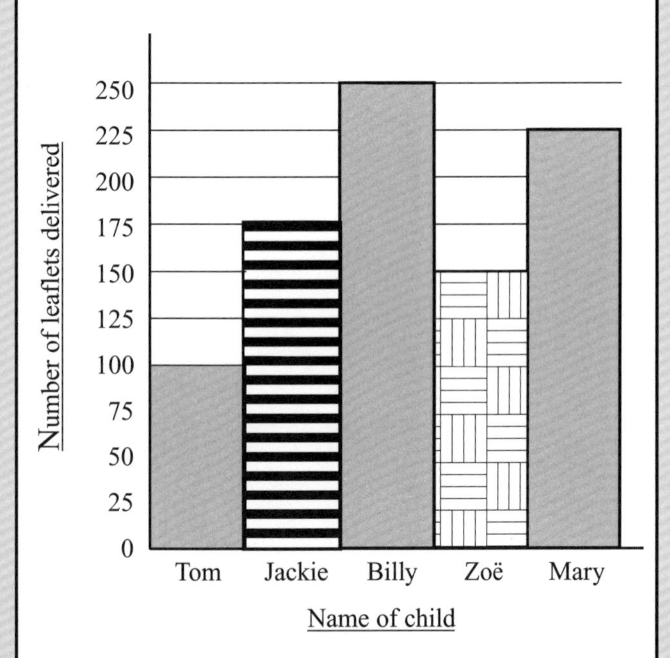

How many more leaflets were delivered by Mary than by Tom?

______

Write your answer in the space provided or mark the appropriate number on your answer sheet.

Question 2

Mr and Mrs Bridge take their three children to the circus. Tickets cost £3.75 each for children. The price of an adult's ticket is £2.50 more than that of a child.

How much does it cost the family to visit the theme park?

£ __________

Write your answer in the space provided or mark the appropriate number on your answer sheet.

Question 3

How many faces would you find on a triangular prism?

______

Write your answer in the space provided or mark the appropriate number on your answer sheet.

Question 4

The ratio of flour to sugar in a cake is 5 : 3.

If 600g of sugar was used to make the cake, how much flour was used?

______

Write your answer in the space provided or mark the appropriate number on your answer sheet.

Question 5

The spinner shown below has an equal chance of landing on any of the numbers.

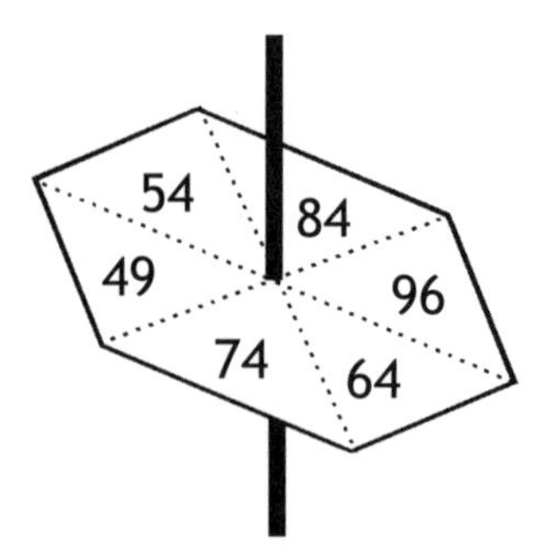

What is the chance that it will come to rest on a number that is a multiple of 7?

Write your answer as a fraction in its lowest possible terms.

______

Write your answer in the space provided or mark the appropriate number on your answer sheet.

Question 6

The hands of the classroom clock show the time 5 o'clock.

What is the smaller angle between the hour hand and the minute hand?

______°

Write your answer in the space provided or mark the appropriate angle on your answer sheet.

Daily Test 5

Score. _______

Question 1

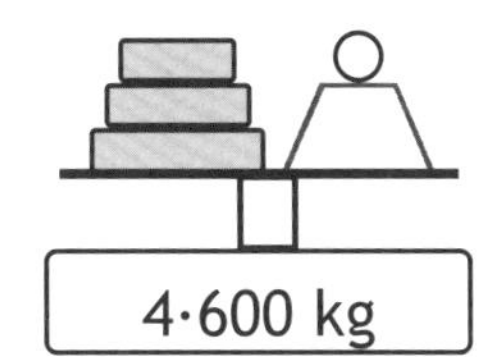

Jenny places some weights on an electronic scale.
She needs to make a total of 5.3 kg.

Which two of the weights below should she choose to make up the weight to the correct amount?

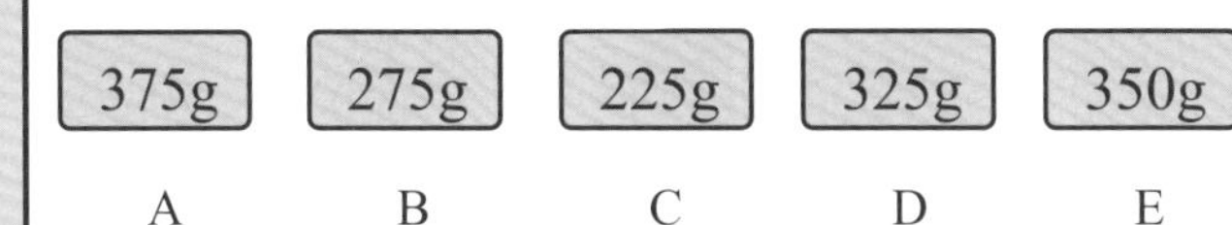

A B C D E

Circle the two appropriate letters below the weights, or mark the two appropriate letters on the answer sheets..

Question 2

Helen and Ian go to an athletics club after school each weekday during the summer term.
They have to pay 70p a day each to attend.
Helen pays an extra 30p a day to have a shower afterwards, whilst Ian waits until he gets home.

How much will it cost the pair of them to go to the athletics club for one week?

£ ________

Write your answer in the space provided or mark the appropriate amount on your answer sheet.

Question 3

Paddington Edgware Road Marylebone Baker Street

A London Underground train ran between Paddington and Baker Street stations.

There were 45 passengers on the train when it left Paddington.
7 people got out at Edgware Road, and 16 people got on.
18 left the train at Marylebone whilst 25 got on.

How many people were on the train at when it arrived at Baker Street?

______

Write your answer in the space provided or mark the appropriate number on your answer sheet.

Question 4

Eric spends y pounds each day on chewing gum. He spends x pounds each week on soft drinks.

How much does Eric spend altogether in one week?

A.	$2y + 5x$	☐
B.	$7x + 7y$	☐
C.	$5y + 2x$	☐
D.	$7x + y$	☐
E.	$x + 7y$	☐

Place a cross in the box next to the correct equation or mark the appropriate letter on your answer sheet.

Question 5

Look at the shape below.

The area of the shaded part is 35cm^2.

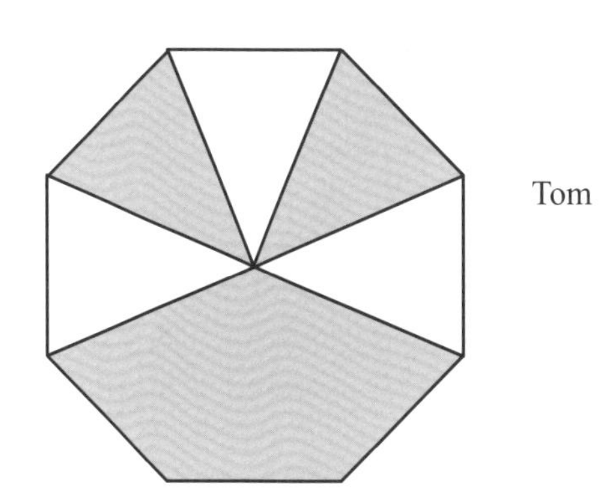

Tom

What is the area of the whole shape?

________ cm^2

Write your answer in the space provided or mark the appropriate number on your answer sheet.

Question 6

Mr Bonner bought 294 small daffodil bulbs for the school garden.
They come packed in boxes of 14.

How many boxes of bulbs did Mr Bonner buy?

_______ boxes

Write your answer in the space provided or mark the appropriate number on your answer sheet.

Daily Test 6

Score. ________

Question 1

In an oil tank there 765 litres of oil.
168 litres were used in February.
148 litres were used in March.

How many litres remain unused?

______ litres

Write your answer in the space provided or mark the appropriate number on your answer sheet.

Question 2

This is a floor plan of the school dining room.

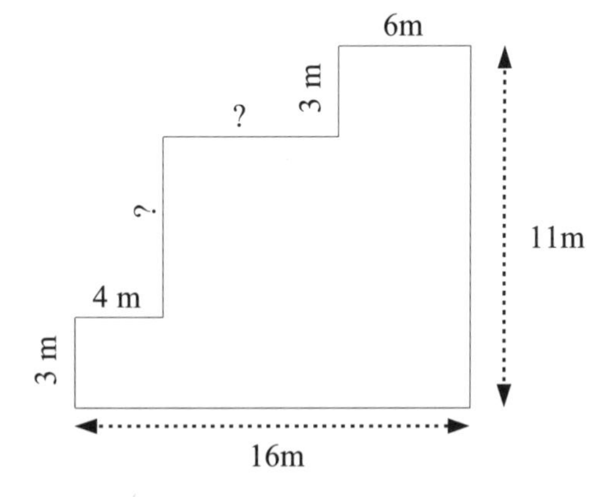

What is the total perimeter of the floor?

_______ m

Write your answer in the space provided or mark the appropriate number on your answer sheet.

Question 3

Michelle is flying to Moscow in Russia to visit her pen friend, Ludmilla.
There is a time difference between Great Britain and Moscow.
Michelle's home in London is 4 hours behind Ludmilla's home in Moscow.
It takes 4 hours to fly from London to Moscow.

If Michelle's plane leaves London at 11am what will the time be in Moscow when her plane touches down?

(Remember to state AM or PM)

____

Write your answer in the space provided or mark the appropriate time on your answer sheet.

Question 4

What fraction of an hour is 40 minutes?

Write your answer in its lowest possible terms.

_____

Write your answer in the space provided or mark the appropriate fraction on your answer sheet.

Question 5

The product of 2 numbers is 72.
The difference between the two numbers is 6.

What are the two numbers?

_____ _____

Write your answers in the space provided or mark the two appropriate numbers on your answer sheet.

Question 6

Look carefully at the graph below.

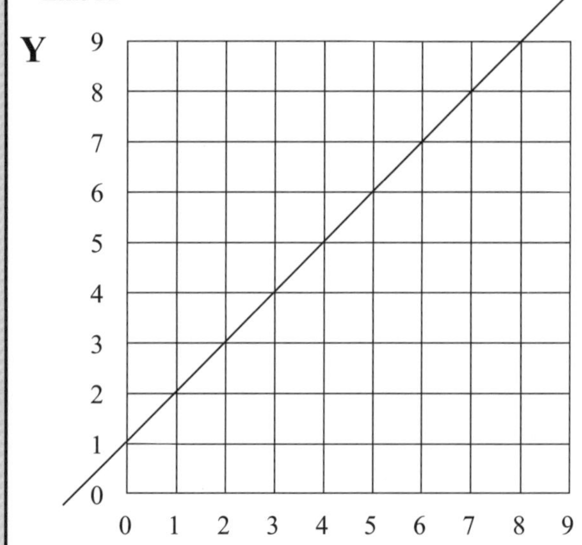

What is the rule that governs the plotting of line A?

Circle the appropriate letter.

A. Y + 2 = X
B. Y - 2 = X
C. 2X = Y + 4
D. X + 1 = Y
E. X x 2 = Y

Write your answer in the space provided or mark the appropriate number on your answer sheet.

Daily Test 7

Score. _______

Question 1

The local computer shop has a sale.
Every item in the shop is reduced by 25%.
Bobby buys a game for his computer.
It normally costs £28.00.

How much does Bobby have to pay for the game in the sale?

£ ___________

Write your answer in the space provided or mark the appropriate number on your answer sheet.

Question 2

Look carefully at the grid below.

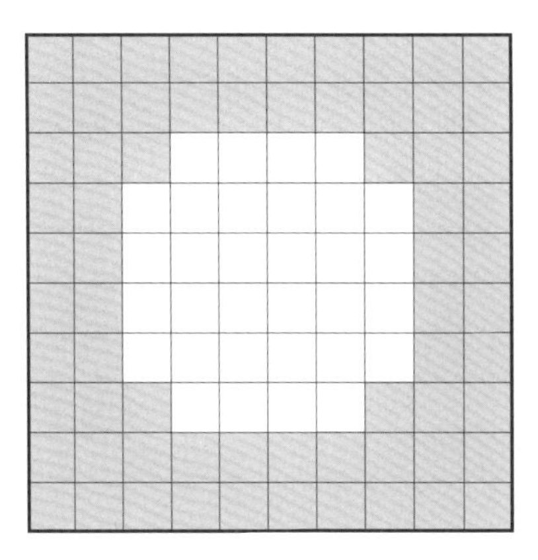

What percentage of this grid has been shaded?

______%

Write your answer in the space provided or mark the appropriate percentage on your answer sheet.

Question 3

Which of the figures below shows the number

thirty-three thousand and three.

A. 33303 ☐
B. 333003 ☐
C. 33003 ☐
D. 3303 ☐
E. 330003 ☐

Place a cross in the box next to the correct number or mark the appropriate letter on your answer sheet.

Question 4

This half term Nicola has taken 7 tables tests. Here are her results out of 20:

14 11 8 16 15 17 10

What was her mean score?

______

Write your answer in the space provided or mark the appropriate number on your answer sheet.

Question 5

Look at the number line below.

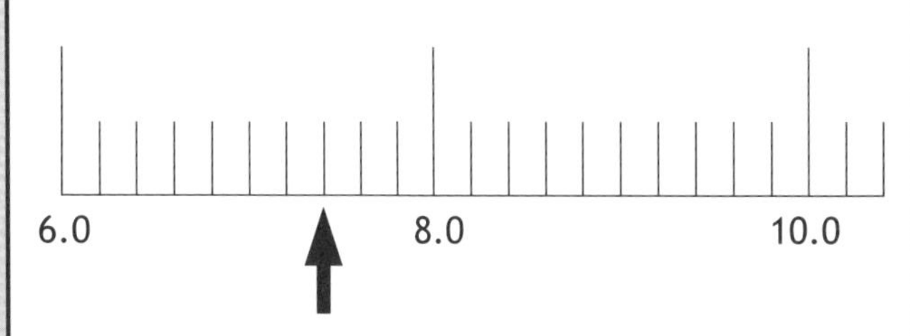

What is the value of the number that the arrow is pointing towards?

______

Write your answer in the space provided or mark the appropriate number on your answer sheet.

Question 6

Mrs Campbell's class did a survey in their school on favourite sports television programmes.

Favourite T.V. Programmes	
Key: □ stands for 6 children ■ stands for 3 children	
World Cup Cricket	□■
Sunday Athletics	□□
Olympic Special	□□□■
World Ice Skating	□□■
FA Cup Football	□□□□■

How many children liked the Olympic Special show?

______

Write your answer in the space provided or mark the appropriate time on your answer sheet.

Daily Test 8

Score. ______

Question 1

Neil and Caroline went to the local shop to buy some party hats for a Christmas party.
In the shop there were 5 different packs at 5 different prices:

A.	Special Paper	£3.80 / pack of 10
B.	Santa Hats	£4.50 / pack of 15
C.	Multicoloured	£4.40 / pack of 20
D.	Assorted	£7.50 / pack of 25
E.	Shiny Silver	£6.00 / pack of 12

Which pack contains the hats at the lowest price each?

A B C D E

Circle the correct letter or mark the appropriate letter on your answer sheet.

Question 2

Rachel, Zoë, Robert and Thomas all stood for election to the school council.

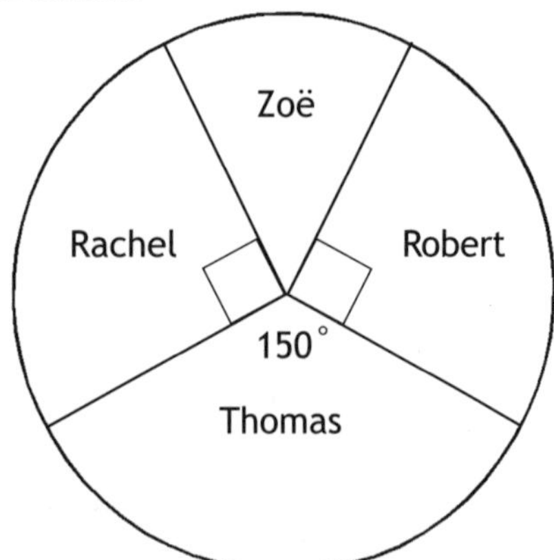

180 children in the school voted for which child they wanted to be their representative on the council.

How many votes did Zoë receive? ________

Write your answer in the space provided or mark the appropriate number on your answer sheet.

Question 3

If $5y + 10 = 25$, then what is the value of y ?

$y =$ _____

Write your answer in the space provided or mark the appropriate number on your answer sheet.

Question 4

Francine, Barbara, Melanie, Justine and Claire each bought a DVD from the local music shop.

Francine paid £7.99, Melanie £8.50, Barbara £12.95, Claire £10.99 and Justine £9.50.

What was the range of the prices paid?

£________

Place a cross in the box or mark the appropriate letter on your answer sheet.

Question 5

Which of these shapes has a rotational symmetry of order 1?

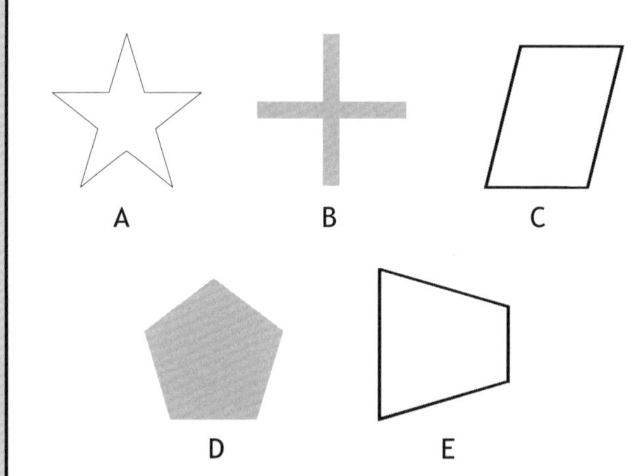

Circle the correct letter/s or mark the appropriate letters on your answer sheet.

Question 6

Mervyn's dad takes Mervyn and his three friends to the pantomime for a treat.

It costs £9.00 for adults and £5.00 each for children. Each child also bought an ice cream and Mervyn's dad had a cup of coffee.

Ice creams are £1.25 each and cups of coffee cost £1.60.

How much did the trip cost Mervyn's dad altogether?

£ __________

Write your answer in the space provided or mark the appropriate amount on your answer sheet.

Daily Test 9

Score. ______

Question 1

Look at the nets below.

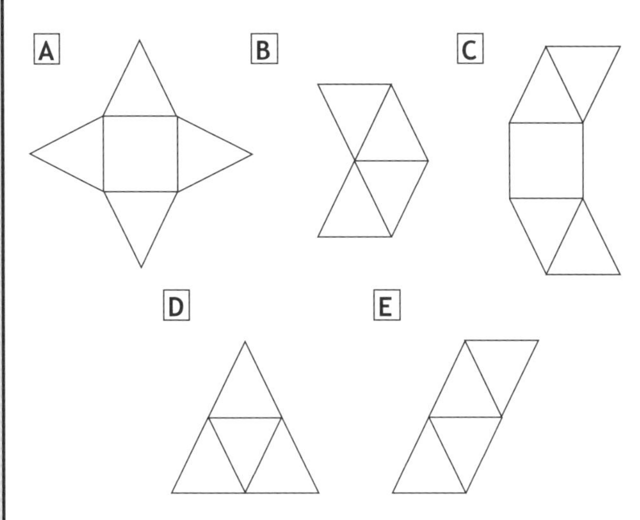

Which of these nets will fold to form a **triangular** based pyramid? There could be more than one.

Circle the letter/s next to the correct net/s or mark the appropriate letters on your answer sheet.

Question 2

Colleen and Sinita go to the Homework Club each weekday evening during the summer term.
They have to pay 80p a day each to attend. Sinita pays an extra 30p a day for a drink, whilst Colleen takes her own.

How much will it cost the pair of them to go to the Homework Club for one week?

£ __________

Write your answer in the space provided or mark the appropriate amount on your answer sheet.

Question 3

Sam's mum buys four, 3 litre bottles of cola from the supermarket.
Approximately how much do the four bottles weigh altogether?

Your answer should be in kilograms.

______Kg

Write your answer in the space provided or mark the appropriate weight on your answer sheet.

Question 4

This is a magic square.

12		14
K		18

All the columns, rows and diagonals add up to 45.

Several numbers have been missed out.

What number should replace the letter ***K*** ?

______

Write your answer in the space provided or mark the appropriate number on your answer sheet.

Question 5

Jane places 9 balls into a black bag. two are red, four are blue and three are yellow.
She takes one ball at random from the bag and places it on the table. It is yellow.

What is the chance that the next ball out of the bag will be red?

$\frac{2}{9}$	$\frac{1}{4}$	$\frac{3}{8}$	$\frac{1}{3}$	$\frac{1}{6}$
A	B	C	D	E

Circle the appropriate letter or mark the appropriate letter on your answer sheet.

Question 6

Look at the numbers below.

Which of the following numbers has a value closest to 10?

9.995	10.899	10.190	9.909	9.992
A	B	C	D	E

Circle the appropriate letter or mark the appropriate number on your answer sheet.

Daily Test 10

Score. _______

Question 1

Three corners of a rectangle have the co-ordinates (6, 6) (1,2) and (1,6).

What are the co-ordinates of the fourth corner?

(____ , ____)

Write your answer in the space provided or mark the appropriate co-ordinates on your answer sheet.

Question 2

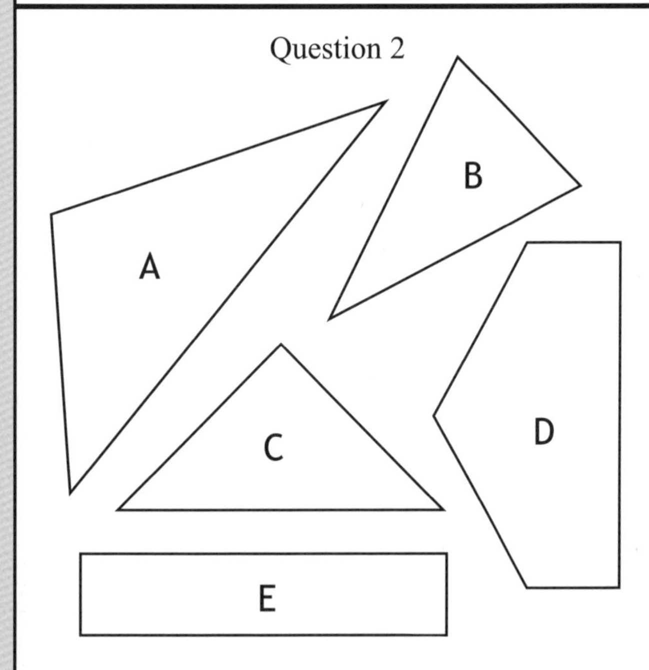

Which of these shapes contains one obtuse angle?

Circle the letter in one of the shapes or mark the appropriate letter on your answer sheet.

Question 3

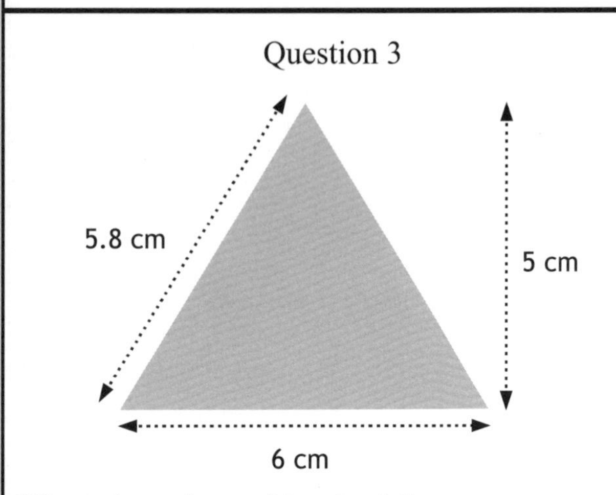

What is the total area of the triangle?

________ cm^2

Write your answer in the space provided or mark the appropriate number on your answer sheet.

Question 4

Look at the graph to the left.

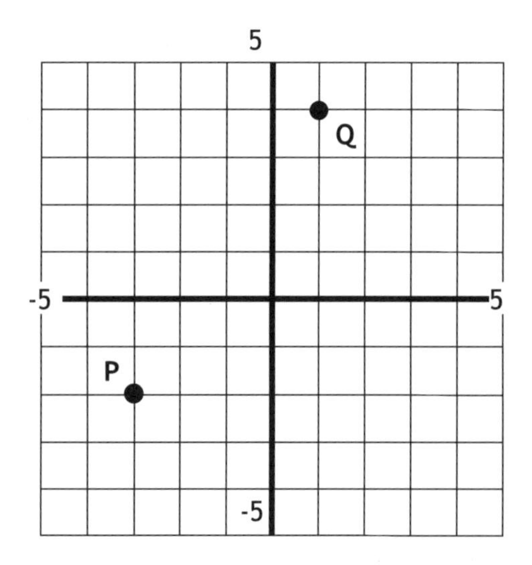

What are the co-ordinates of P and Q?

	P	Q	
A.	(-2, -3)	(4, 1)	☐
B.	(-2, -1)	(1, 4)	☐
C.	(-3, 2)	(3, 1)	☐
D.	(-3, -2)	(1, 4)	☐
E.	(2, -3)	(4, 1)	☐

Place a cross in the correct box or mark the appropriate letter on your answer sheet.

Question 5

Look at the following number.

10.7561

What is this number to 2 (two) decimal places?

____

Place a cross in the box or mark the appropriate letter on your answer sheet.

Question 6

Complete the following sequence:

5, 15, 35, 45, 65, ______

Write your answer in the space provided or mark the appropriate number on your answer sheet.

Daily Test 11

Score. _______

Question 1

Eric spends x pounds each week on sweets. He spends y pounds each month on magazines.

How much does Eric spend altogether in one year?

A. $12y + 52x$ ☐

B. $12x + 7y$ ☐

C. $5y + 52x$ ☐

D. $7x + 52y$ ☐

E. $12x + 52y$ ☐

Place a cross in the box next to the correct equation or mark the appropriate letter on your answer sheet.

Question 2

Look at the shape below.

The area of the shaded part is 35cm^2.

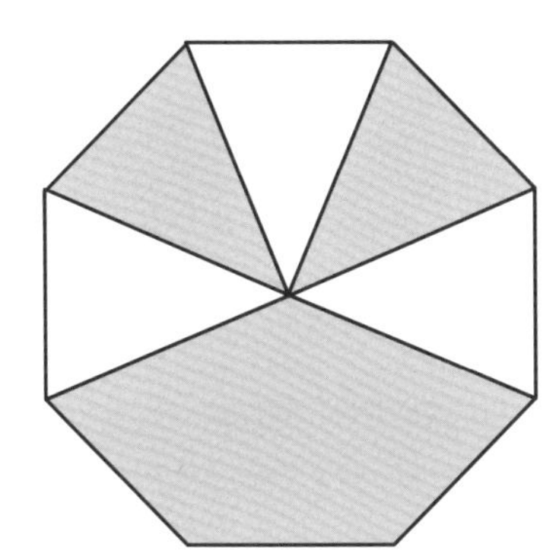

What is the area of the unshaded part?

________ cm^2

Write your answer in the space provided or mark the appropriate number on your answer sheet.

Question 3

Mr Jennings bought 342 party hats for the school Christmas party.
They come packed in boxes of 18.

How many boxes of party hats did Mr Jennings buy?

_______ boxes

Write your answer in the space provided or mark the appropriate number on your answer sheet.

Question 3

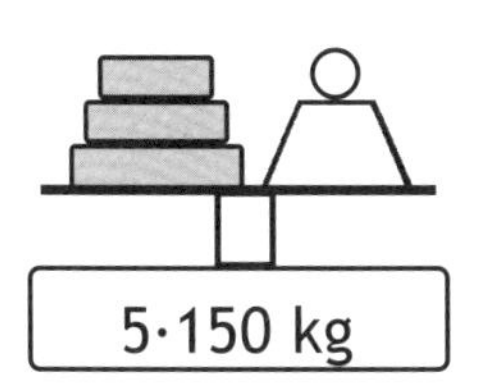

Jenny places some weights on an electronic scale.
She needs to make a total of 5.8 kg.

Which two of the weights below should she choose to make up the weight to the correct amount?

325g	275g	225g	375g	350g
A	B	C	D	E

Circle the two appropriate letters below the weights, or mark the two appropriate letters on the answer sheets..

Question 5

Simone and Barry go to the burger bar each weekday during half term week.
They each pay £1.20 for a burger.
They spend an extra 90p a day for some fries, which they share.

How much does it cost the pair of them to go to the burger bar during the week?

£ ________

Write your answer in the space provided or mark the appropriate amount on your answer sheet.

Question 6

Paddington — Edgware Road — Marylebone — Baker Street

A London Underground train ran between Paddington and Baker Street stations.

There were 50 passengers on the train when it left Paddington.
27 people got out at Edgware Road, and 14 people got on.
8 left the train at Marylebone whilst 25 got on.

How many people were on the train at Baker Street?

______

Write your answer in the space provided or mark the appropriate number on your answer sheet.

Daily Test 12

Score. _______

Question 1

The ratio of flour to sugar in a cake is 5 : 3.

If 450g of sugar was used to make the cake, how much flour was used?

_______ grams

Write your answer in the space provided or mark the appropriate number on your answer sheet.

Question 2

The spinner shown below has an equal chance of landing on any of the numbers.

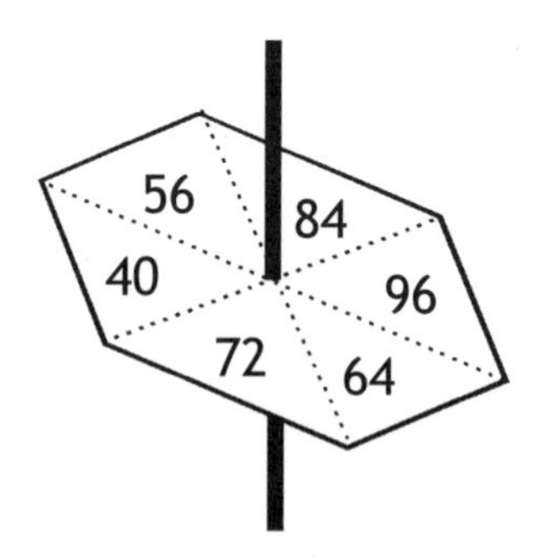

What is the chance that it will come to rest on a number that is a multiple of 6?

Write your answer as a fraction in its lowest possible terms.

_____

Write your answer in the space provided or mark the appropriate number on your answer sheet.

Question 3

The hands of the classroom clock show the time 4 o'clock.

What is the reflex angle between the hour hand and the minute hand?

______°

Write your answer in the space provided or mark the appropriate angle on your answer sheet.

Question 4

Mrs Davis keeps a record of all cakes sold in the school canteen in a week. The bar chart below shows how many cakes were sold in a particular week.

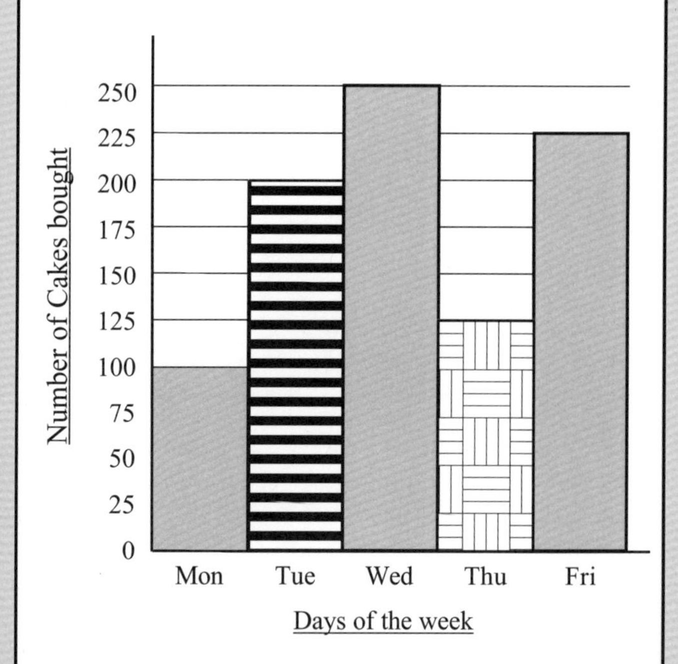

How many more cakes were bought on Wednesday than on Monday?

_____

Write your answer in the space provided or mark the appropriate number on your answer sheet.

Question 5

Mr and Mrs Jackson take their four children to a rugby match. Tickets cost £7.50 each for adults. The price of a child's ticket is £2.75 less than that of an adult.

How much does it cost the family to see the rugby match?

£ ________

Write your answer in the space provided or mark the appropriate number on your answer sheet.

Question 6

How many faces would you find on a dodecahedron?

_____

Write your answer in the space provided or mark the appropriate number on your answer sheet.

Daily Test 13

Score. ______

Question 1

This is Jenny's function machine.

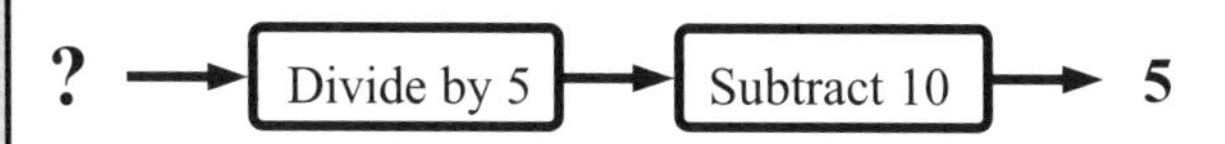

What number did she start with?

______

Write your answer in the space provided or mark the appropriate number on your answer sheet.

Question 2

Alice, Mark, Helen and Jessica all stood for election to be captain of the school quiz team.

200 children in the school voted for which girl they wanted to be the captain. The percentages of votes cast are shown in the pie chart below.

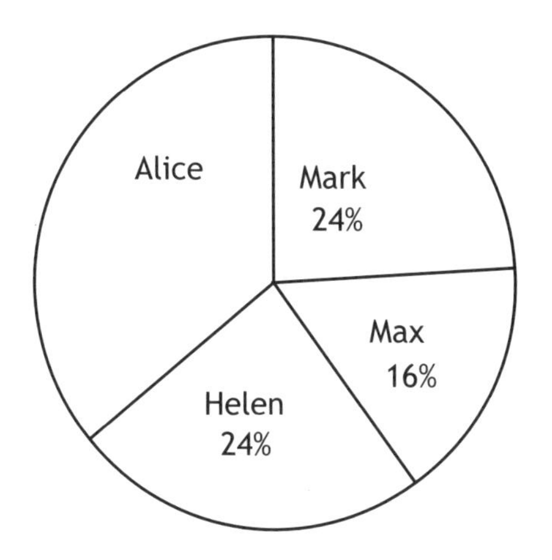

How many votes did Alice receive? ______

Write your answer in the space provided or mark the appropriate number on your answer sheet.

Question 3

How should 11.30 at night be written in the 24 hour clock?

______

Write your answer in the space provided or mark the appropriate time on your answer sheet.

Question 4

Look at the net below. When folded it makes a box.

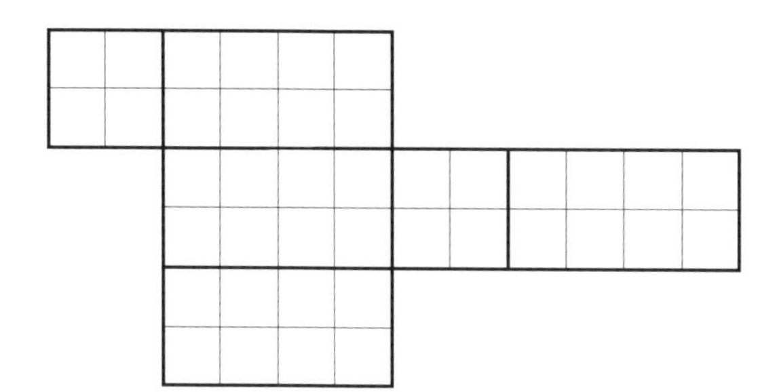

If each small square has an area of 5 cm^2 what will be the total surface area of the box?

______ cm^2

Write your answer in the space provided or mark the appropriate number on your answer sheet.

Question 5

There are 48 children on a train. 16 girls and 32 boys. One child's name is chosen at random to collect the tickets.

What is the chance that the child will be a boy?

(Show your answer as a fraction in its lowest terms.)

______

Write your answer in the space provided or mark the appropriate number on your answer sheet.

Question 6

180 children took part in a "Guess teacher's age" competition.

$\frac{5}{9}$ guessed too high. $\frac{1}{4}$ guessed too low.

How many children guessed the correct age of the teacher?

______

Write your answer in the space provided or mark the appropriate number on your answer sheet.

Daily Test 14

Score. ________

Question 1

Jenny has the job of totalling the money collected in the charity tins. Today she has four tins to check, containing £1.99, £7.63, £14.65 and £8.93.

How much was collected in all four tins?

£ __________

Place a cross in the box or mark the appropriate letter on your answer sheet.

Question 2

This graph shows the conversion rate between Swiss Francs (f) and UK Pounds (£).

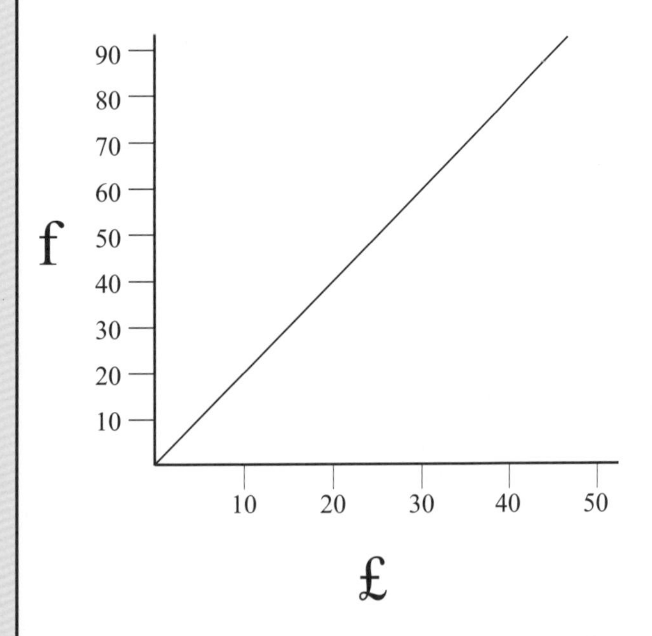

How many pounds (£) would I need to change to get f 80?

£ ______

Write your answer in the space provided or mark the appropriate number on your answer sheet.

Question 3

Ufton Junior played the Smithton Primary in a football match.
The match kicked off at 2.20 p.m. They played 25 minutes each half, and had a half-time break of 20 minutes.

At what time did the match end? __________

Write your answer in the space provided or mark the appropriate time on your answer sheet.

Question 4

Leonora has five 50 pence pieces, two 20 pence pieces, a ten pence piece and two 5 pence pieces in her pocket.

How much money does she have in total?

£ ____________

Write your answer in the space provided or mark the appropriate number on your answer sheet.

Question 5

This is a map of the tunnels under Morton Castle. You must try to find your way from the dining room to the lounge using a set of instructions.

Key to the instructions:
FD means forward, **RT** means turn right 90º and **LT** means turn left 90º.

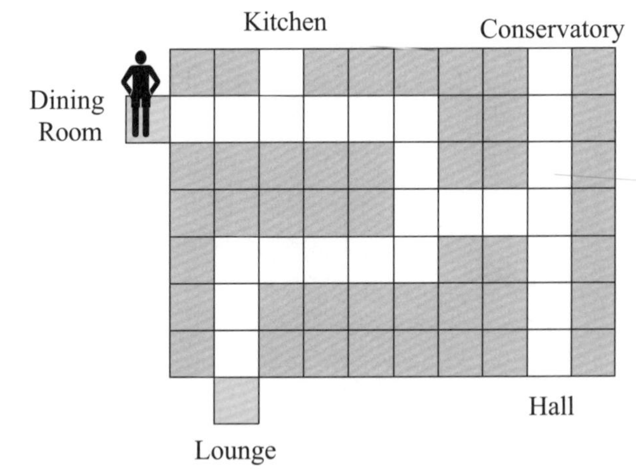

Which of these sets of instructions is the correct one? Circle the appropriate letter or mark the appropriate letter on your answer sheet.

A. FD 6, LT, FD 3, LT, FD 4, RT, FD 3.

B. FD 6, RT, FD 4, RT, FD 3, LT, FD 4.

C. FD 6, RT, FD 3, LT, FD 4, RT, FD 3.

D. FD 6, RT, FD 3, RT, FD 4, LT, FD 3.

E. FD 5, RT, FD 3, RT, FD 5, LT, FD 3.

Question 6

Bob's mother is 4 times as old as Bob was 2 years ago.

If Bob is 9, then how old is his mother? ________

Write your answer in the space provided or mark the appropriate number on your answer sheet.

Daily Test 15

Score. ________

Question 1

Which of these sets of numbers contains all square numbers?

A. 4 9 18 ☐
B. 12 16 35 ☐
C. 18 27 64 ☐
D. 16 36 81 ☐
E. 25 99 121 ☐

Place a cross in the box or mark the appropriate letter on your answer sheet.

Question 2

Look at the Venn diagram below. It shows how many children in Mrs Blade's class like sausages, mashed potato or both. 4 children like neither. There are 32 children in the class. Some numbers are missing.

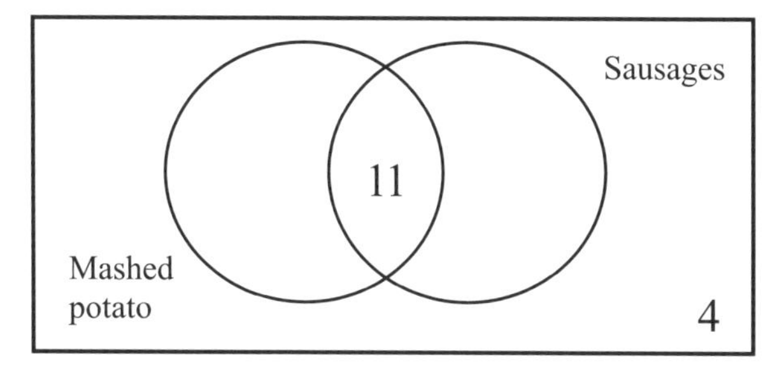

If 23 children like mashed potato and 16 like sausages:

How many children in the class like only mashed potato?

(______)

Write your answer in the space provided or mark the appropriate number on your answer sheet.

Question 3

In this question you must find the missing number so that the equation balances.

$4 \times 8 + 20 = 5 \times 5 +$ ________

Write your answer in the space provided or mark the appropriate number on your answer sheet.

Question 4

13	26	39
26	39	52
39	52	

There is a number missing on this grid.

What is it? (_____)

Write your answer in the space provided or mark the appropriate number on your answer sheet.

Question 4

Look at the diagram below:

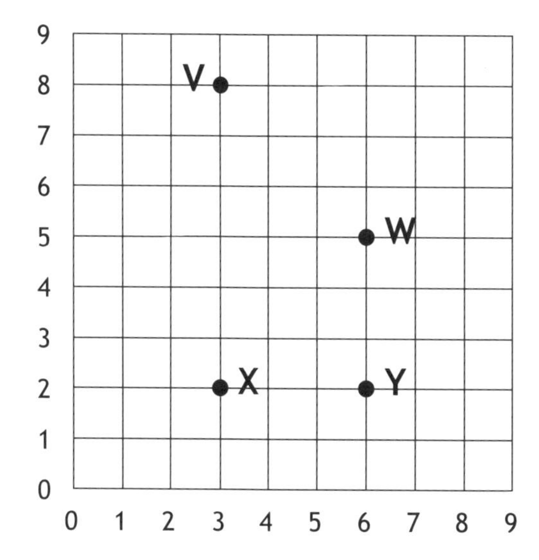

What are the co-ordinates of the points at letter X and letter W?

W ____ , ____

X ____ , ____

Write the co-ordinates in the spaces provided or mark the appropriate pair your answer sheet.

Question 6

There are 12 fairy cakes in a packet.

How many packets would you fill with 372 cakes?

________ packets

Write your answer in the space provided or mark the appropriate number on your answer sheet.

Daily Test 16

Score. ________

Question 1

Look at the graph to the left.

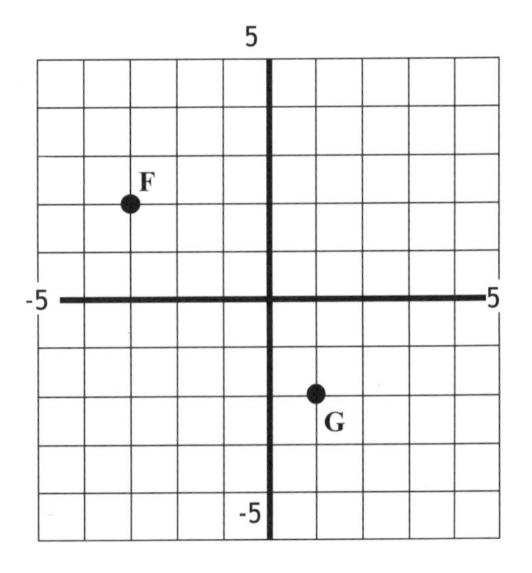

What are the co-ordinates of F and G?

	F	G	
A.	(-2, 1)	(3, 2)	☐
B.	(-3, 2)	(1, -2)	☐
C.	(-3, -2)	(2, -1)	☐
D.	(1, -2)	(-2, 3)	☐
E.	(-3, 2)	(-1, -2)	☐

Place a cross in the correct box or mark the appropriate letter on your answer sheet.

Question 2

Look at the following number.

59.095

What is this number to 1 (one) decimal places?

____

Place a cross in the box or mark the appropriate letter on your answer sheet.

Question 3

Complete the following sequence:

7, 14, 22, 31, 41, ______

Write your answer in the space provided or mark the appropriate number on your answer sheet.

Question 4

Three corners of a rectangle have the co-ordinates (3, 2) (5, 9) and (3, 9).

What are the co-ordinates of the fourth corner?

(____ , ____)

Write your answer in the space provided or mark the appropriate co-ordinates on your answer sheet.

Question 5

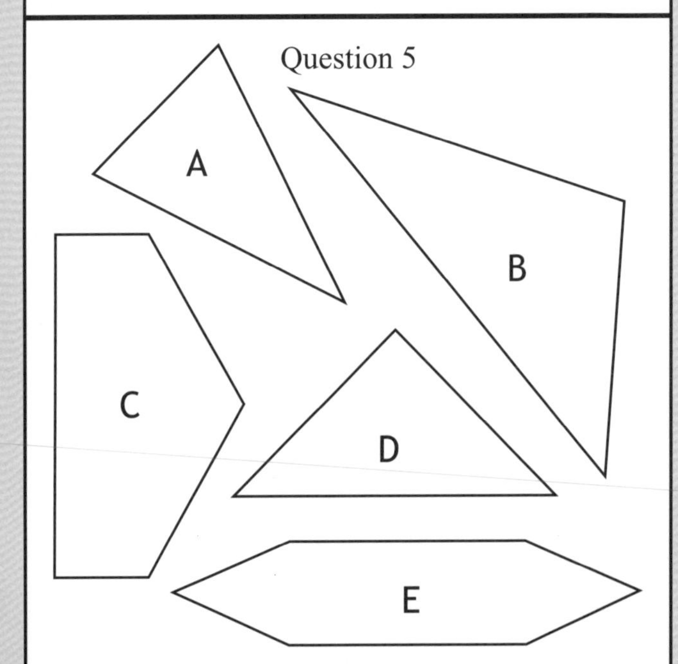

Which one of the shapes above has only one obtuse angle?

Circle the letter in one of the shapes or mark the appropriate letter on your answer sheet.

Question 6

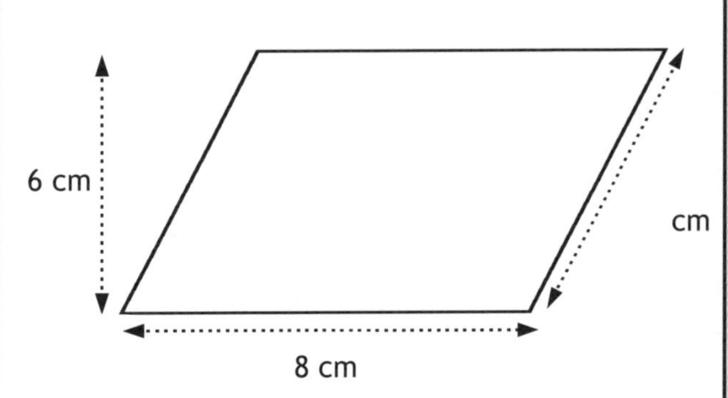

What is the total area of the parallelogram?

________ cm^2

Write your answer in the space provided or mark the appropriate number on your answer sheet.

Daily Test 17

Score. _______

Question 1

This is a magic square.

21		19
	P	15

All the columns, rows and diagonals add up to 54.

Several numbers have been missed out.

What number should replace the letter ***P*** ?

____

Write your answer in the space provided or mark the appropriate number on your answer sheet.

Question 2

Rebecca places 10 balls into a black bag. three are red, two are green and five are blue.
She takes one ball at random from the bag and places it on the table. It is blue.

What is the chance that the next ball out of the bag will be another blue?

$\frac{4}{9}$	$\frac{5}{9}$	$\frac{3}{8}$	$\frac{1}{2}$	$\frac{3}{7}$
A	B	C	D	E

Circle the appropriate letter or mark the appropriate letter on your answer sheet.

Question 3

Catherine and Alex go to the Holiday Club each weekday morning during the summer.
They have to pay £1.60 a day each to attend. Alex pays an extra 40p a day for a drink, whilst Catherine takes her own.

How much will it cost the pair of them to go to Holiday Club for one week?

£ _________

Write your answer in the space provided or mark the appropriate amount on your answer sheet.

Question 4

Look at the nets below.

A
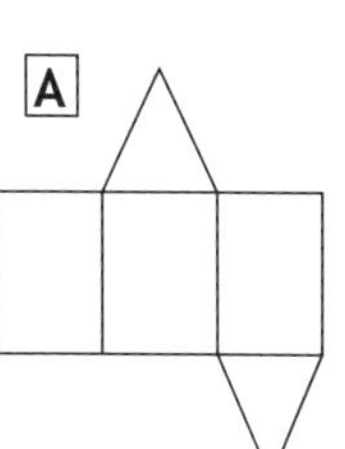

B
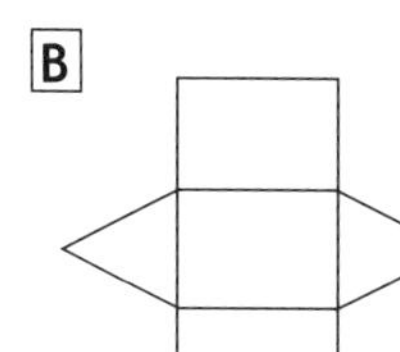

C
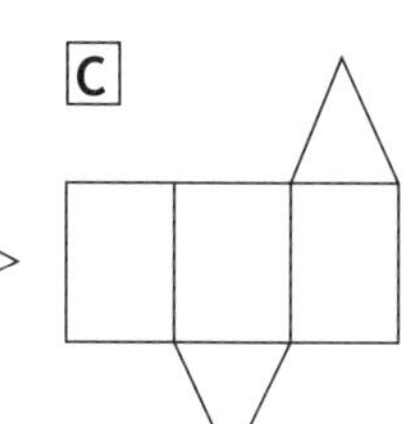

D
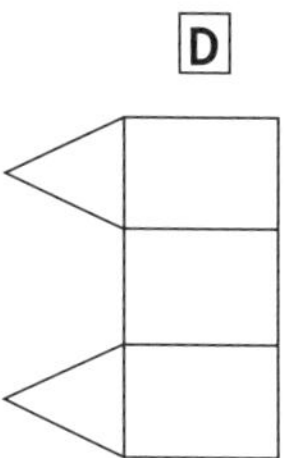

E
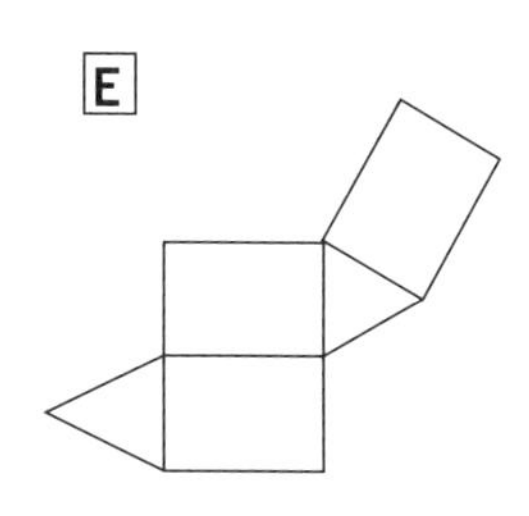

Which one of these nets will NOT fold to form a **triangular** prism?

Circle the letter next to the correct net or mark the appropriate letter on your answer sheet.

Question 5

Look at the numbers below.

100.089	99.098	99.982	100.099	99.098
A	B	C	D	E

Which of the following numbers has a value closest to 100?

Circle the appropriate letter or mark the appropriate number on your answer sheet.

Question 6

Freda's dad buys five, 6 litre bottles of spring water from the supermarket.
Approximately how much do they weigh altogether?

Your answer should be in kilograms.

_______Kg

Write your answer in the space provided or mark the appropriate weight on your answer sheet.

Daily Test 18

Score. ________

Question 1

James, Sally, Kathryn, Rory and Cheryl each bought a computer game from the local shop.

James paid £15.00, Kathryn £16.30, Rory £11.95, Cheryl £8.95 and Sally £9.50.

What was the range of the prices paid?

£______

Place a cross in the box or mark the appropriate letter on your answer sheet.

Question 2

Which of these shapes has a rotational symmetry of order 4?

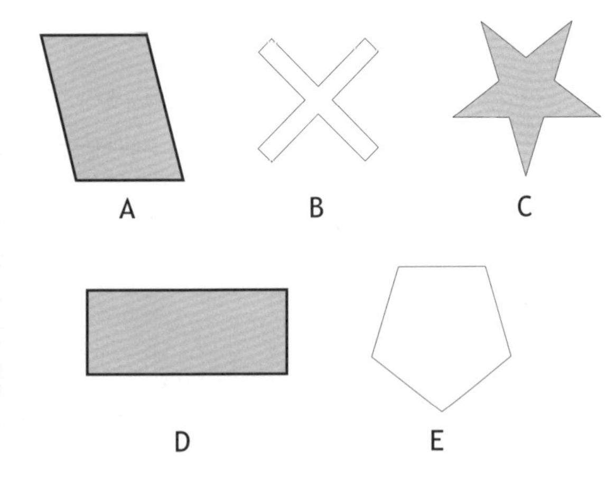

Circle the correct letter/s or mark the appropriate letters on your answer sheet.

Question 3

Rachel's uncle takes Rachel and her two friends to Paris for a treat.

It costs £54.00 for adults and £28.00 each for children. They each have lunch on the train

Lunches cost £5.00 each.

How much did the trip cost Rachel's uncle altogether?

£ ________

Write your answer in the space provided or mark the appropriate amount on your answer sheet.

Question 4

Sammy and Rebecca went to the local shop to buy some crackers for a Christmas party.
In the shop there were 5 different packs at 5 different prices:

A.	Big Bang crackers	£3.45 / pack of 10
B.	Reindeer Red crackers	£2.40 / pack of 8
C.	Santa Special crackers	£4.80 / pack of 20
D.	Magic Elf crackers	£7.50 / pack of 25
E.	Standard crackers	£3.20 / pack of 16

Which pack contains the crackers at the lowest price each?

A B C D E

Circle the correct letter or mark the appropriate letter on your answer sheet.

Question 5

Billy, Françoise, Jamal and Zoë all collected money for a disaster appeal.

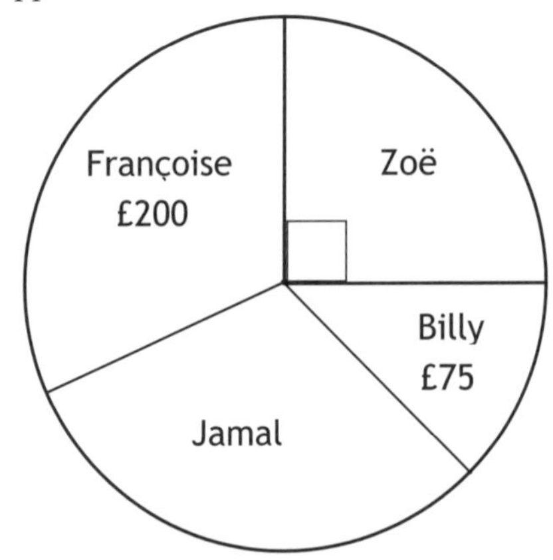

Between them they collected £600. They drew a pie chart to show how much each of them had collected.

How much did Jamal collect? £ _____

Write your answer in the space provided or mark the appropriate number on your answer sheet.

Question 6

If $4x + 8 = 32$, then what is the value of x ?

$x =$ _____

Write your answer in the space provided or mark the appropriate number on your answer sheet.

Daily Test 19

Score. ______

Question 1

This half term Saeeda has taken 7 tables tests. Here are her results out of 20:

16 13 19 15 12 18 12

What was her mean score?

______

Write your answer in the space provided or mark the appropriate number on your answer sheet.

Question 2

Look at the number line below.

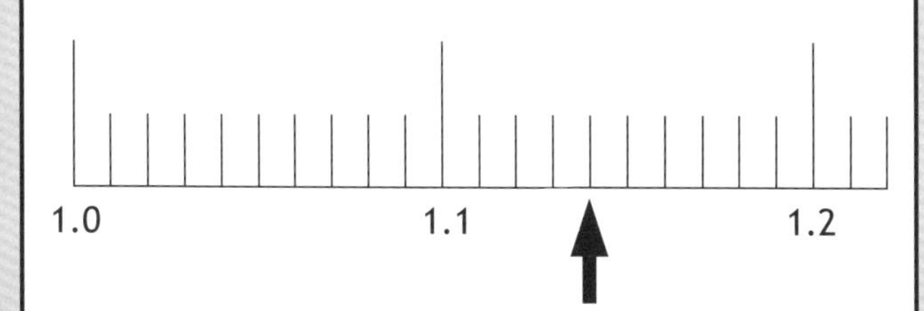

What is the value of the number that the arrow is pointing towards?

______

Write your answer in the space provided or mark the appropriate number on your answer sheet.

Question 3

Mrs Campbell's class did a survey in their school on favourite ice creams.

Favourite Ice Creams	
Key: □ stands for 5 children ■ stands for 1 child	
Raspberry Ripple	□■■■
Cornish Vanilla	□□■
Chocolate Fudge	□□□■■■
Peanut Surprise	□□■
Choc'n'mint	□□□■■

How many children liked the Choc'n'mint flavour?

______

Write your answer in the space provided or mark the appropriate time on your answer sheet.

Question 3

The local furniture shop has a sale.
Every item in the shop is reduced by 25%.
Mrs Sibley buys a new sofa for her sitting room.
It normally costs £360.00.

How much does Mrs Sibley have to pay for the game in the sale?

£ ______

Write your answer in the space provided or mark the appropriate number on your answer sheet.

Question 5

Look carefully at the grid below.

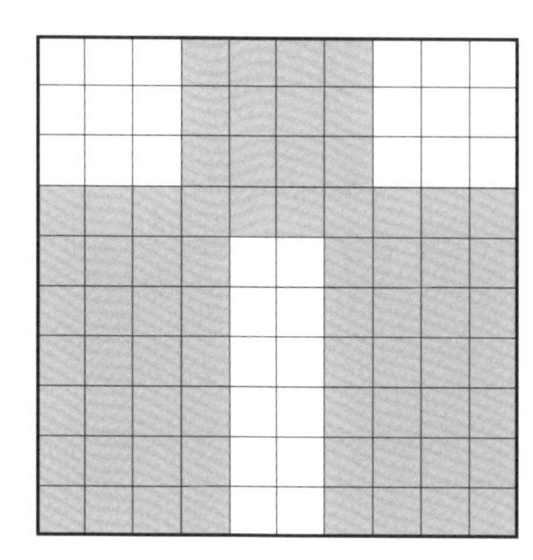

What percentage of this grid has been shaded?

______%

Write your answer in the space provided or mark the appropriate percentage on your answer sheet.

Question 6

Which of the figures below shows the number

Sixty-six thousand and sixteen.

A. 660016 □
B. 60616 □
C. 66016 □
D. 66160 □
E. 6616 □

Place a cross in the box next to the correct number or mark the appropriate letter on your answer sheet.

Daily Test 20

Score. ________

Question 1

What fraction of a day is 18 hours?

Write your answer in its lowest possible terms.

______

Write your answer in the space provided or mark the appropriate fraction on your answer sheet.

Question 2

The product of 2 numbers is 45.

The difference between the two numbers is 12.

What are the two numbers?

______ ______

Write your answers in the spaces provided or mark the appropriate numbers on your answer sheet.

Question 3

Look carefully at the graph below.

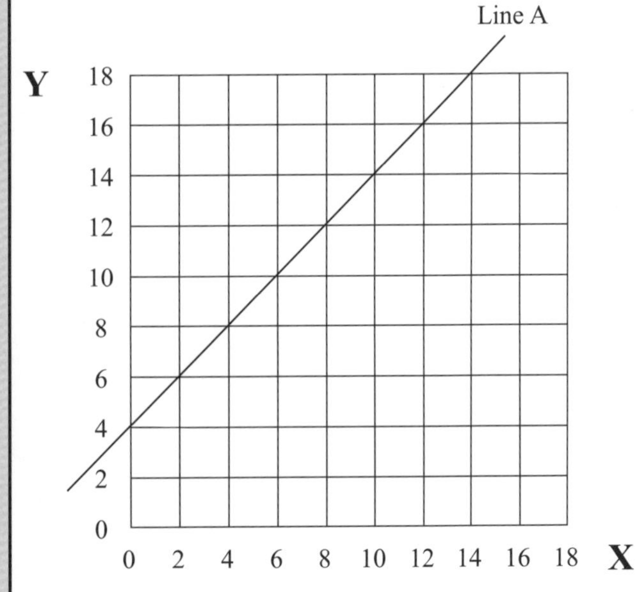

What is the rule that governs the plotting of line A?

Circle the appropriate letter.

A. X = Y - 4

B. X = Y + 8

C. 2X = Y + 2

D. X + 5 = Y

E. Y = 2X + 2

Write your answer in the space provided or mark the appropriate number on your answer sheet.

Question 4

In a factory there are 900 boxes of CDs.
238 are sold to High Street music shops.
123 are sold to internet shops.

How many boxes remain unsold?

______ boxes

Write your answer in the space provided or mark the appropriate number on your answer sheet.

Question 5

This is a floor plan of the school dining room.

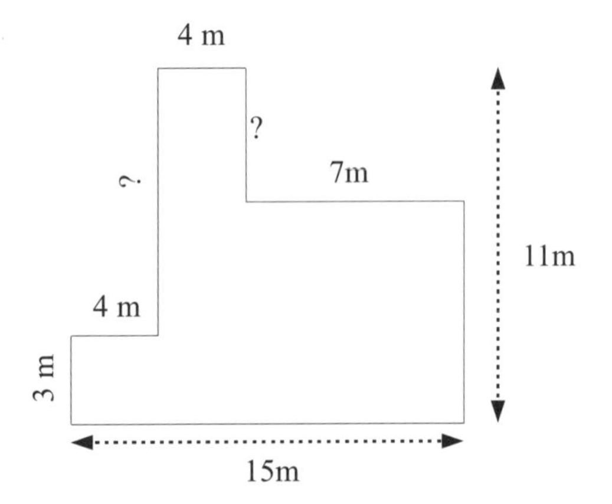

What is the total perimeter of the floor?

______ m

Write your answer in the space provided or mark the appropriate number on your answer sheet.

Question 6

Geraldine is flying to Florida for a holiday with her family. She is looking forward to visiting the theme parks. There is a time difference between Great Britain and Florida in the United States.
Geraldine's home in London is 5 hours ahead of Florida in the US.
It takes 9 hours to fly from London to Florida.

If Geraldine's plane leaves London at 10am what will the time be in Florida when her plane touches down?

(Remember to state AM or PM)

____

Write your answer in the space provided or mark the appropriate time on your answer sheet.

Multiple choice answer sheet. Tests 1 to 6.

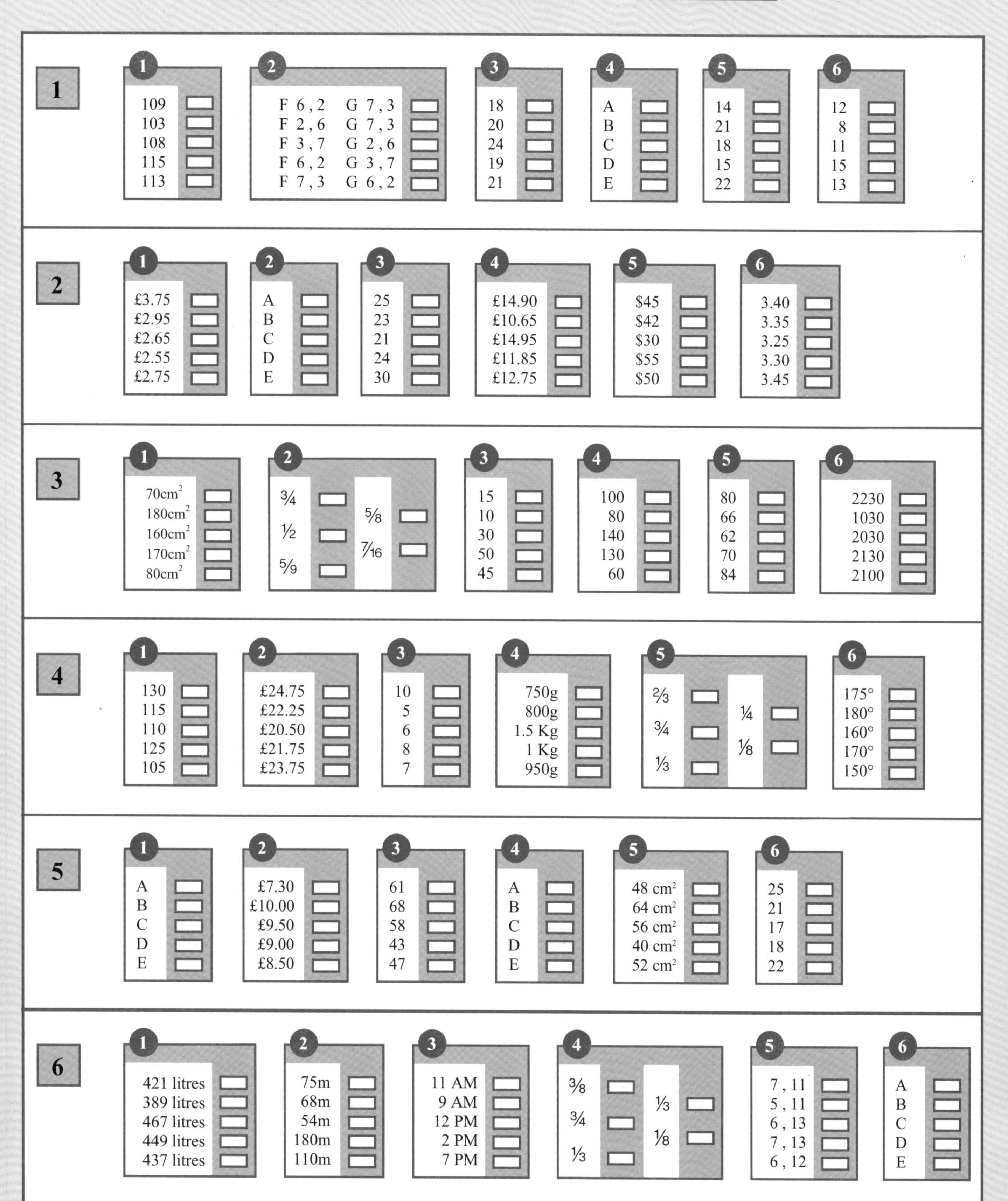

1

1	2	3	4	5	6
109	F 6 , 2 G 7 , 3	18	A	14	12
103	F 2 , 6 G 7 , 3	20	B	21	8
108	F 3 , 7 G 2 , 6	24	C	18	11
115	F 6 , 2 G 3 , 7	19	D	15	15
113	F 7 , 3 G 6 , 2	21	E	22	13

2

1	2	3	4	5	6
£3.75	A	25	£14.90	$45	3.40
£2.95	B	23	£10.65	$42	3.35
£2.65	C	21	£14.95	$30	3.25
£2.55	D	24	£11.85	$55	3.30
£2.75	E	30	£12.75	$50	3.45

3

1	2	3	4	5	6
70cm^2	¾	15	100	80	2230
180cm^2	½	10	80	66	1030
160cm^2	5⁄9	30	140	62	2030
170cm^2	5⁄8	50	130	70	2130
80cm^2	7⁄16	45	60	84	2100

4

1	2	3	4	5	6
130	£24.75	10	750g	⅔	175°
115	£22.25	5	800g	¾	180°
110	£20.50	6	1.5 Kg	⅓	160°
125	£21.75	8	1 Kg	¼	170°
105	£23.75	7	950g	⅛	150°

5

1	2	3	4	5	6
A	£7.30	61	A	48 cm^2	25
B	£10.00	68	B	64 cm^2	21
C	£9.50	58	C	56 cm^2	17
D	£9.00	43	D	40 cm^2	18
E	£8.50	47	E	52 cm^2	22

6

1	2	3	4	5	6
421 litres	75m	11 AM	⅜	7 , 11	A
389 litres	68m	9 AM	¾	5 , 11	B
467 litres	54m	12 PM	⅓	6 , 13	C
449 litres	180m	2 PM	⅓	7 , 13	D
437 litres	110m	7 PM	⅛	6 , 12	E

Multiple choice answer sheet. Tests 7 to 12.

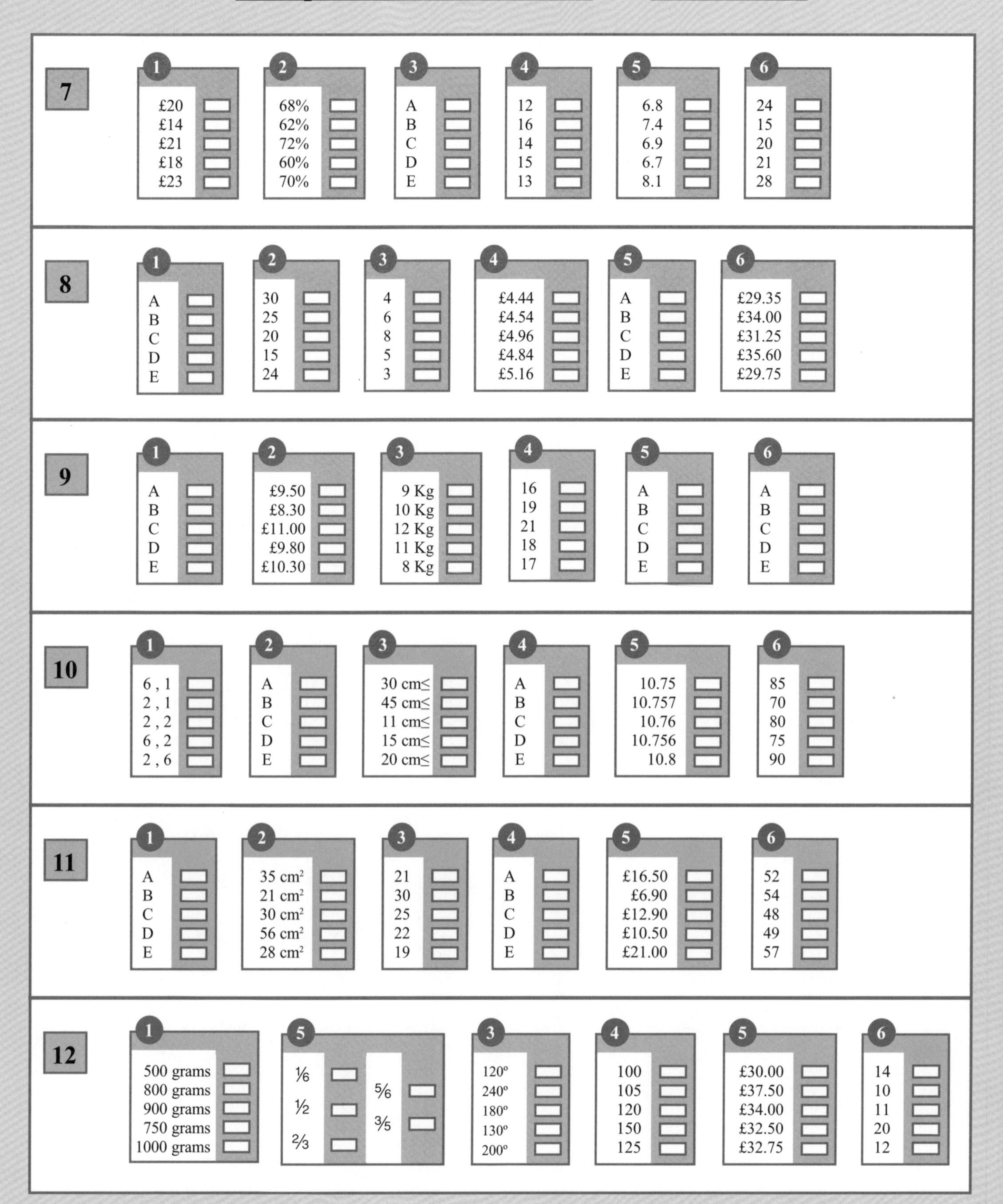

7

1	2	3	4	5	6
£20	68%	A	12	6.8	24
£14	62%	B	16	7.4	15
£21	72%	C	14	6.9	20
£18	60%	D	15	6.7	21
£23	70%	E	13	8.1	28

8

1	2	3	4	5	6
A	30	4	£4.44	A	£29.35
B	25	6	£4.54	B	£34.00
C	20	8	£4.96	C	£31.25
D	15	5	£4.84	D	£35.60
E	24	3	£5.16	E	£29.75

9

1	2	3	4	5	6
A	£9.50	9 Kg	16	A	A
B	£8.30	10 Kg	19	B	B
C	£11.00	12 Kg	21	C	C
D	£9.80	11 Kg	18	D	D
E	£10.30	8 Kg	17	E	E

10

1	2	3	4	5	6
6 , 1	A	30 cm≤	A	10.75	85
2 , 1	B	45 cm≤	B	10.757	70
2 , 2	C	11 cm≤	C	10.76	80
6 , 2	D	15 cm≤	D	10.756	75
2 , 6	E	20 cm≤	E	10.8	90

11

1	2	3	4	5	6
A	35 cm^2	21	A	£16.50	52
B	21 cm^2	30	B	£6.90	54
C	30 cm^2	25	C	£12.90	48
D	56 cm^2	22	D	£10.50	49
E	28 cm^2	19	E	£21.00	57

12

1	5	3	4	5	6
500 grams	⅙	120°	100	£30.00	14
800 grams	½	240°	105	£37.50	10
900 grams	⅔	180°	120	£34.00	11
750 grams	⅚	130°	150	£32.50	20
1000 grams	⅗	200°	125	£32.75	12

Multiple choice answer sheet. Tests 13 to 18.

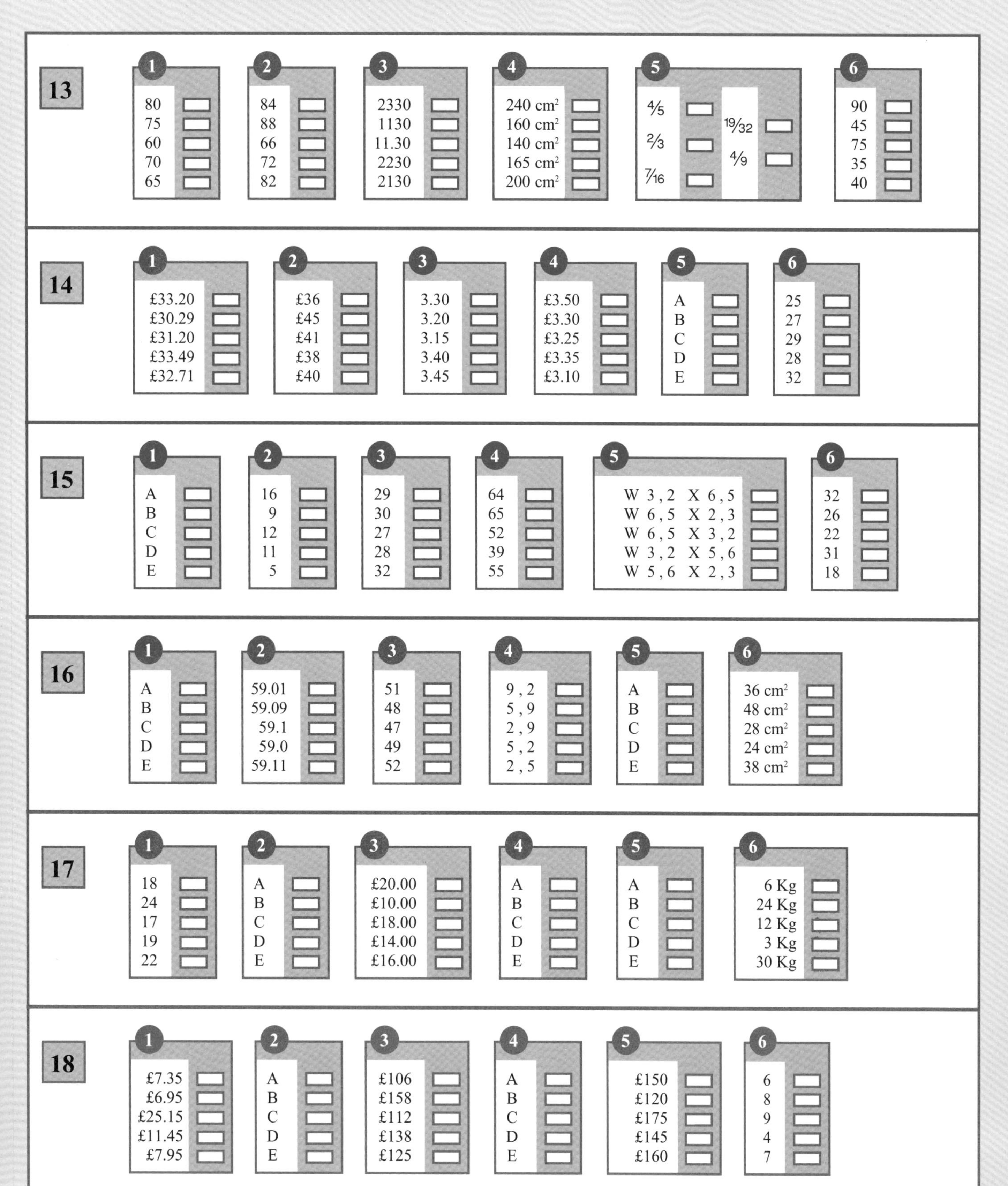

13

1	2	3	4	5	6
80	84	2330	240 cm^2	$\frac{4}{5}$	90
75	88	1130	160 cm^2	$\frac{2}{3}$	45
60	66	11.30	140 cm^2	$\frac{7}{16}$	75
70	72	2230	165 cm^2	$\frac{19}{32}$	35
65	82	2130	200 cm^2	$\frac{4}{9}$	40

14

1	2	3	4	5	6
£33.20	£36	3.30	£3.50	A	25
£30.29	£45	3.20	£3.30	B	27
£31.20	£41	3.15	£3.25	C	29
£33.49	£38	3.40	£3.35	D	28
£32.71	£40	3.45	£3.10	E	32

15

1	2	3	4	5	6
A	16	29	64	W 3 , 2 X 6 , 5	32
B	9	30	65	W 6 , 5 X 2 , 3	26
C	12	27	52	W 6 , 5 X 3 , 2	22
D	11	28	39	W 3 , 2 X 5 , 6	31
E	5	32	55	W 5 , 6 X 2 , 3	18

16

1	2	3	4	5	6
A	59.01	51	9 , 2	A	36 cm^2
B	59.09	48	5 , 9	B	48 cm^2
C	59.1	47	2 , 9	C	28 cm^2
D	59.0	49	5 , 2	D	24 cm^2
E	59.11	52	2 , 5	E	38 cm^2

17

1	2	3	4	5	6
18	A	£20.00	A	A	6 Kg
24	B	£10.00	B	B	24 Kg
17	C	£18.00	C	C	12 Kg
19	D	£14.00	D	D	3 Kg
22	E	£16.00	E	E	30 Kg

18

1	2	3	4	5	6
£7.35	A	£106	A	£150	6
£6.95	B	£158	B	£120	8
£25.15	C	£112	C	£175	9
£11.45	D	£138	D	£145	4
£7.95	E	£125	E	£160	7

Multiple choice answer sheet. Tests 19 & 20.

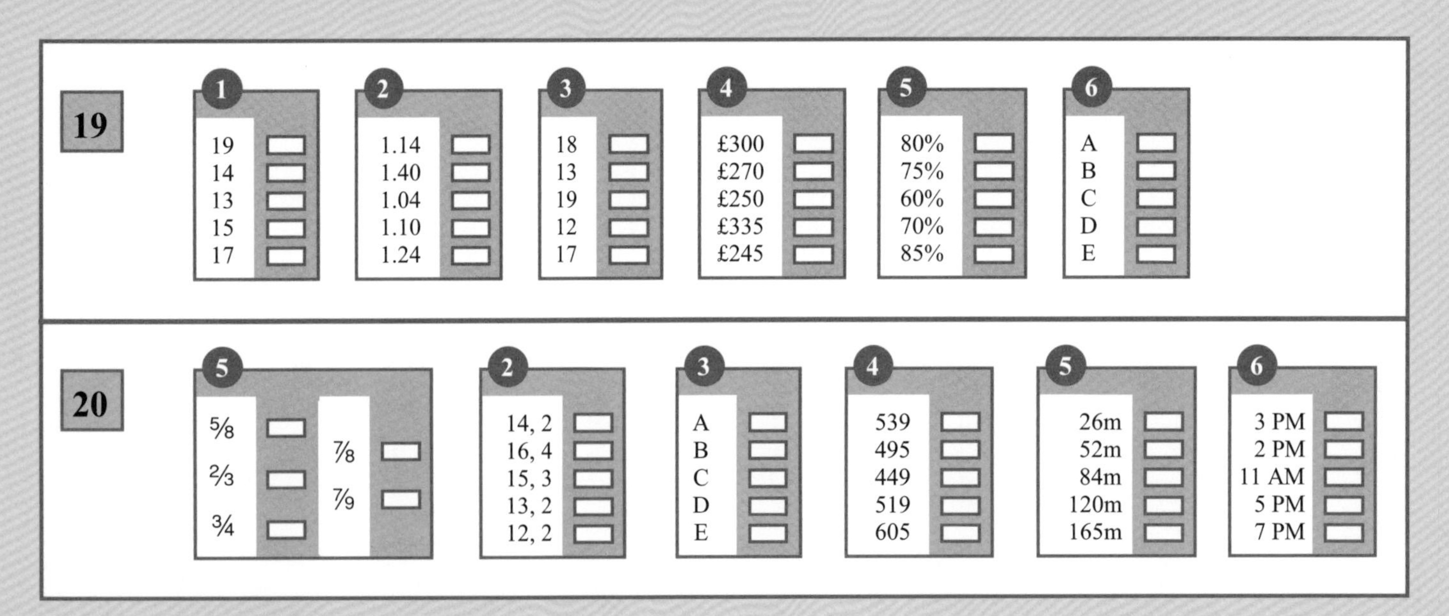

19

1: 19, 14, 13, 15, 17

2: 1.14, 1.40, 1.04, 1.10, 1.24

3: 18, 13, 19, 12, 17

4: £300, £270, £250, £335, £245

5: 80%, 75%, 60%, 70%, 85%

6: A, B, C, D, E

20

5: ⅝, ⅔, ¾, ⅞, 7⁄9

2: 14, 2; 16, 4; 15, 3; 13, 2; 12, 2

3: A, B, C, D, E

4: 539, 495, 449, 519, 605

5: 26m, 52m, 84m, 120m, 165m

6: 3 PM, 2 PM, 11 AM, 5 PM, 7 PM

Answers

	Test 1	Test 2	Test 3	Test 4	Test 5
1	113	£2.65	160cm^2	125	A & D
2	F 6,2 G 3,7	D	5/9	£23.75	£8.50
3	20	21	15	5	61
4	D	£14.90	60	1 Kg	E
5	21	$45	70	⅓	56 cm^2
6	11	3:35pm	2230 hrs	150°	21

	Test 6	Test 7	Test 8	Test 9	Test 10
1	449	£21	C	B & D	6 , 2
2	54m	68%	15	£9.50	A
3	7 PM	C	3	12 Kg	15 cm^2
4	⅔	13	£4.96	16	D
5	6 & 12	7.4	E	B	10.76
6	D	21	£35.60	A	75

	Test 11	Test 12	Test 13	Test 14	Test 15
1	A	750 grams	75	£33.20	D
2	21 cm^2	½	72	£40	12
3	19	240°	2330 hrs	3:30pm	27
4	B & D	150	200 cm^2	£3.10	65
5	£16.50	£34.00	⅔	D	W 6,5 X 3,2
6	54	12	35	28	31

	Test 16	Test 17	Test 18	Test 19	Test 20
1	B	22	£7.35	15	¾
2	59.1	A	B	1.14	15 & 3
3	52	£18.00	£158.00	17	A
4	5 , 2	D	E	£270.00	539
5	B	C	£175.00	70%	52m
6	48 cm^2	30 Kg	6	C	2 PM